Play-along for Clarinet
GOSPEL

Wise Publications
part of The Music Sales Group
London/New York/Paris/Sydney/Copenhagen/Berlin/Madrid/Hong Kong/Tokyo

Published by
Wise Publications
14-15 Berners Street, London W1T 3LJ, UK.

Exclusive Distributors:
Music Sales Limited
Distribution Centre, Newmarket Road, Bury St Edmunds,
Suffolk IP33 3YB, UK.
Music Sales Pty Limited
20 Resolution Drive, Caringbah, NSW 2229, Australia.

Order No. AM997084
ISBN: 978-1-84938-022-5
This book © Copyright 2010 Wise Publications,
a division of Music Sales Limited.

Music engravings supplied by Camden Music.
Edited by Lizzie Moore.

Printed in the EU.

CD recorded, mixed and mastered by Jonas Persson.
Clarinet played by Howard McGill.

Your Guarantee of Quality:
As publishers, we strive to produce every book to
the highest commercial standards.
The music has been freshly engraved and the book has been
carefully designed to minimise awkward page turns and
to make playing from it a real pleasure.
Particular care has been given to specifying acid-free, neutral-sized
paper made from pulps which have not been elemental chlorine bleached.
This pulp is from farmed sustainable forests and was
produced with special regard for the environment.
Throughout, the printing and binding have been planned to
ensure a sturdy, attractive publication which should give years of enjoyment.
If your copy fails to meet our high standards,
please inform us and we will gladly replace it.

www.musicsales.com

Clarinet Fingering Chart

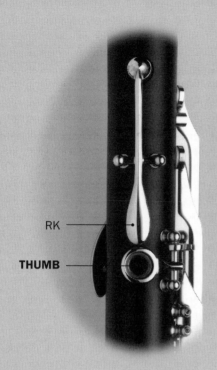

RK

THUMB

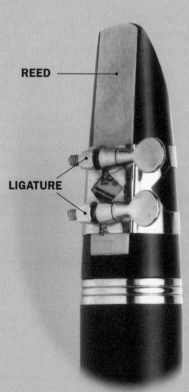

REED

LIGATURE

Mouthpiece

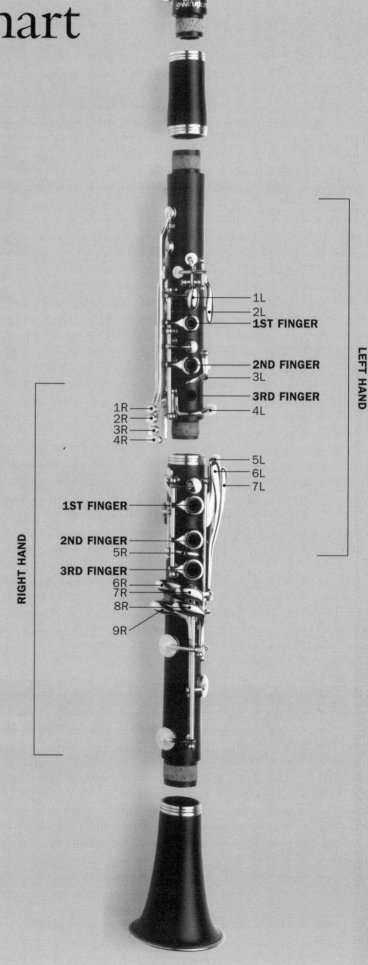

1L
2L
1ST FINGER

2ND FINGER
3L

3RD FINGER
4L

1R
2R
3R
4R

5L
6L
7L

1ST FINGER

2ND FINGER
5R

3RD FINGER

6R
7R
8R
9R

LEFT HAND

RIGHT HAND

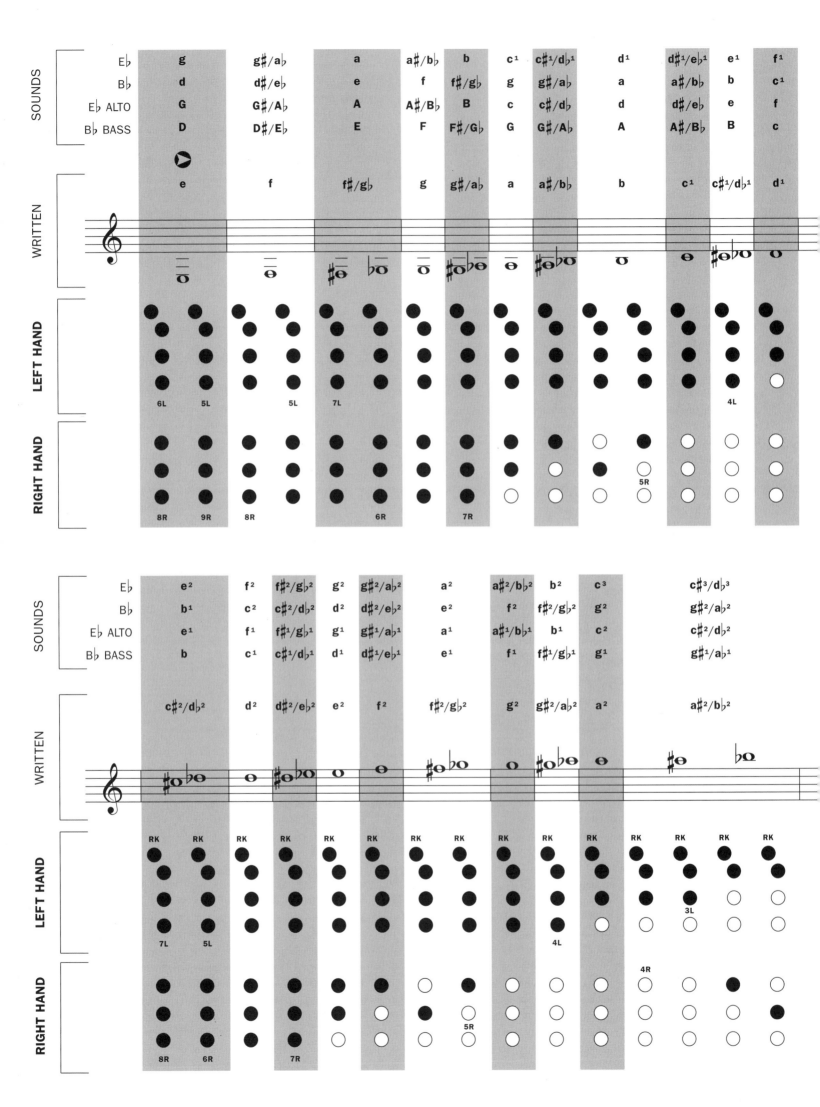

Indicates the lower limit of the best playing range for E♭, B♭, E♭ Alto and B♭ Bass Clarinets

Indicates the upper limit of the best playing range for E♭ and B♭ Clarinets

Indicates the upper limit of the best playing range for E♭ Alto and B♭ Bass Clarinets

Amazing Grace

Words & Music by John Newton

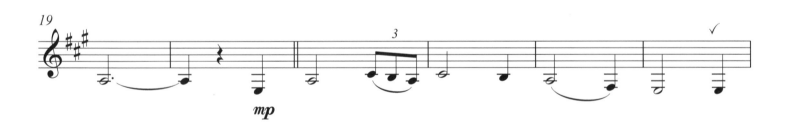

Down By The Riverside

Traditional

9

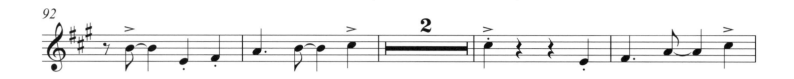

D.S. al Coda   **Coda**

Go Down Moses

Traditional

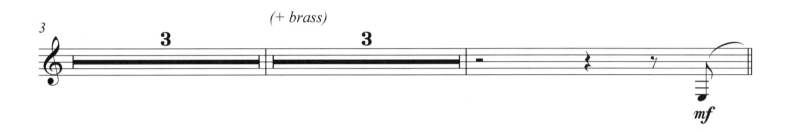

I Found The Answer

Words & Music by Johnny Lange

Just A Closer Walk With Thee

Traditional

molto rit.

Lean On Me

Words & Music by Bill Withers

(There'll Be) Peace In The Valley (For Me)

Words & Music by Thomas A. Dorsey

Sometimes I Feel Like A Motherless Child

Traditional

Swing Low, Sweet Chariot

Traditional

(organ solo)

When The Saints Go Marching In

Traditional

molto rit.

123456789

Bringing you the words and the music

All the latest music in print... rock & pop plus jazz, blues, country, classical and the best in West End show scores.

- Books to match your favourite CDs.

- Book-and-CD titles with high quality backing tracks for you to play along to. Now you can play guitar or piano with your favourite artist... or simply sing along!

- Audition songbooks with CD backing tracks for both male and female singers for all those with stars in their eyes.

- Can't read music? No problem, you can still play all the hits with our wide range of chord songbooks.

- Check out our range of instrumental tutorial titles, taking you from novice to expert in no time at all!

- Musical show scores include *The Phantom Of The Opera*, *Les Misérables*, *Mamma Mia* and many more hit productions.

- DVD master classes featuring the techniques of top artists.

CD Track Listing

1. **Tuning Notes**

   Full instrumental performances...

2. Amazing Grace
   (Newton) Dorsey Brothers Music Ltd.

3. Down By The Riverside
   (Trad) Dorsey Brothers Music Ltd.

4. Go Down Moses
   (Trad) Dorsey Brothers Music Ltd.

5. I Found The Answer
   (Lange) Campbell Connelly & Company Ltd.

6. Just A Closer Walk With Thee
   (Trad) Dorsey Brothers Music Ltd.

7. Lean On Me
   (Withers) Universal/MCA Music Ltd.

8. (There'll Be) Peace In The Valley
   (For Me)
   (Dorsey) Carlin Music Corporation

9. Sometimes I Feel Like A
   Motherless Child
   (Trad) Dorsey Brothers Music Ltd.

10. Swing Low, Sweet Chariot
    (Trad) Dorsey Brothers Music Ltd.

11. When The Saints Go Marching In
    (Trad) Dorsey Brothers Music Ltd.

Backing tracks only...

12. Amazing Grace

13. Down By The Riverside

14. Go Down Moses

15. I Found The Answer

16. Just A Closer Walk With Thee

17. Lean On Me

18. (There'll Be) Peace In The Valley
    (For Me)

19. Sometimes I Feel Like A
    Motherless Child

20. Swing Low, Sweet Chariot

21. When The Saints Go Marching In

MCPS

To remove your CD from the plastic sleeve, lift the small lip to break the perforations.
Replace the disc after use for convenient storage.